The American Farmer

The American Farmer

*A glimpse into the world
and heart of the
American food grower
and his family;
shaped by all seasons,
sustained by
a belief in Spring*

BY RICHARD K. SEIM

PHOTOGRAPHY: CHARLES BRILL

RAND McNALLY & COMPANY
Chicago/New York/San Francisco

DEDICATED
to Carroll P. Streeter.
During a quarter
century with Farm Journal,
he taught his staff
(including me) to think
of farmers first as human
beings who love, work,
play and worship.

Book design by PAUL M. PANOC

Copyright © 1974 by Farm Journal, Inc.

Library of Congress Catalog Card Number 74-13903

All Rights Reserved

Printed in United States of America

Photographs by Charles Brill except pages 13, 15, 61, 99, 122-23, 124-25, 129, 130-31, 160, 174, 186 Richard K. Seim; 100 Bob Hawks; 154 Libby Photographers; 174 Jack Goodson.

First printing, September, 1974
Second printing, December, 1974

When you believe in Spring...

I Spring

> You sow...

II Summer

> And grow...

III Autumn

> And harvest...

IV Winter

> And plan it all again
> while winter dances
> white and black, and
> noses freeze, and fires
> crack, and dark earth
> waits on sleeping seed
> and warming sun, and rain

A way of life...

You count a food grower among your ancestors. Your father? Grandfather? His father? Back through the years...

He grew steel arms guiding a plow, squeezing cows' teats, flashing an axe. In a good year, what he grew fed his wife and children until the next harvest. As he prospered, or his sons, good years brought something to put by. Money to buy the shaped steel that ate more acres, and more. And that bought time to read, then more steel, and more acres...Now some sons could walk out of the furrow—some eagerly, some reluctantly, but off the land.

As we moved into the 1970's, our food grower, the American farmer, had so mastered agricultural applications of mechanical, chemical and electronic technology that a relative handful of men, their wives and children fed over 200 million of us. And traded a great part of their production over the oceans, besides.

So farming has become a business, not a way of life. Or so the experts say. But the statement rings only half true. Oh, farming has earned the title: big business, tremendous business. Only possession and use of business skills allow survival, and quick minds shape industrial concepts to crop and animal production. Today's farmer pays a price in study and work to stay on the land, to enjoy farming-the-way-of-life.

It *is* a way of life. Different. Exciting. Good. In a time when millions yearn to reach back to a world lost to them—back to the whip of tall grass against bare legs, foaming cloud parades across a scrubbed blue sky, the gritty sweetness of a patch-picked berry—the farmer can still whoop to an infinity of sky when the day brings happiness. Or on a black day, squeeze comfort from a handful of soil, while the whole open earth absorbs his tears.

Bright day or black, you know who you are, there between soil and sky. You wear a man's clothes, rough and heavy. You look, you feel, you smell like a man. You know you're a man. And you live with the sort of man you are. For there's no hiding your fields, your cattle, your orchards.

No other man knows the full sweep of smells and sounds and sights that nature rushes past you, season after season. The raw-earth smell of birth; the sweet, sensual musk of flowering corn in the hot liquid air of July; the husbandman's pure pleasure in watching cattle eat; the star music and the brittle rasp of snow underfoot on a zero-still winter night. And yes, the desolation of a grain field swept by hail, or the acrid smell of baby pig disease, wringing life from tiny bodies; twisting your own gut with fear and loss.

Farmer…stockman. Homely names for men caught up in a still romantic pursuit of life, balancing everything against nature each year, each season, each storm. Men with a kernel of optimism that sprouts hope after every loss, so long as skill equals challenge—and a banker will believe.

Farming a business? Certainly. But the farmer's time-clock moves with the seasons, and ties him to the earth. And that eternal movement paces a way of life with the same rich rewards to senses and spirit that your food-growing ancestors knew. Follow the American farmer around the sun in these pages. You'll come to know something of the heart and spirit of a man who believes in spring.

SPRING

"You sow..."

You tickle your big rig through the field gate, swing the folded implement "wings" into place with a finger touch of hydraulic power, settle steel to the earth… and in that instant's pause, you have the power to declare spring! Your hand slaps fuel to the engine, and it's here. Real spring, stirring the winter-mellowed soil, snugging seed into the damp earth—corn, cotton, wheat, pregnant shoots of vegetables and fruits. No more seed catalog itch, no more false starts—soft pink mornings that mask a sneaky freeze. It's spring, real spring again, and soon green life in the field will match the squealing, bawling new life in your barns.

Power...horsepower...too much power,
some experts say. Well, we have too
many firetrucks, too—until there's
a fire. Nature allots you *almost*
enough fine weather each year for
plowing and planting and harvest.
So you need power, plenty of it, to
get the big jobs done on time.

...the throaty diesel sings to you;
the wheel feels good in your
hands after the winter layoff. And
the soil stirs smooth as cream
beneath the surface crust.

But a day of sunshine can draw rain
clouds like flies to honey.

So you live in a hurry
at planting time…driving yourself with
pleasurable impatience through this
season of new beginnings

...feeding hungry planters
the seed and fertilizer and chemicals
that you ribbon between
sunrise and sunset.

The stored chill of winter still seeps
into the day when the sun dims. But
the soil works right; so you roll.

Then you wait.
And worry.
And lose the seed to cold,
or bugs, or too much rain,
or too little
…in your mind.

But the northbound sun's warm
fingers probe deeper each day.
Swelling seed responds with pale green
flags of life, and soon you can
"row" the crop. And you find reasons
to inspect it, over and over, as if
it were a new baby.

You do "father" each crop.

Rejoice in its birth, suffer through its setbacks,

take pride in its mature promise.

Patience, pleasure and pain;
rewards for devotion to parenthood.
The same bright sun that warms new
life tracks early age across your
face. Who counts that cost? Or
hands etched deep by wind and wet...

...when new hearts beat beneath
your touch, or young plants root
and grow.

Your hands can make the difference...

a calf breathes; a cow lives

because you were there.

"Does she think the pail is her mama, Grampa?"

I like pigs; like working with them…
always have, ever since I waded
around after my dad. Oh, you've got to *think*
to succeed. But you can still help
yourself with your hands.

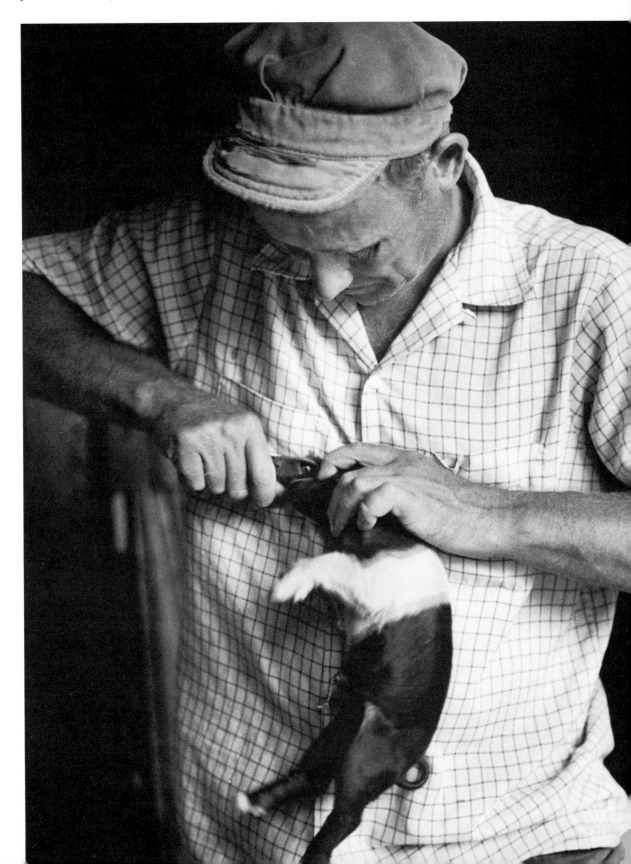

28

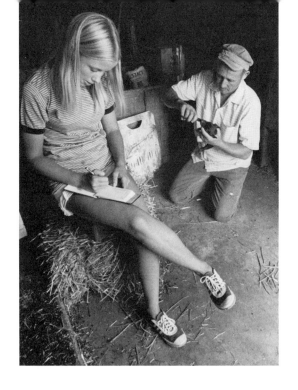

"There's plenty of hand work
starting little pigs off right. It gives
the kids a chance to help, too...

"You know one of the
best things about farming?
You've got your wife
and kids and work all wrapped
together, all in one spot
...all at home.
You can't have that in
many other businesses."

"…I guess we all look forward to big moments in
our lives. In your daydreams, they don't happen
when you're wearing old jeans and wishing you had
a tissue to wipe the baby's nose. But some of them
do occur in everyday life—the best ones, I've come to
think. Like today…just an hour's hike with the kids.
But it was a soft morning, and you could smell the
new year in the fresh-worked soil. And we were
…well, we were all in tune…"

"We really did a job on that
driveway. I smile when I look at it now.
But we were all a part of it;
everybody helped. And so long as it lasts,
the kids will remember that, when they
look for their marks along the edge."

Those little faces glow fresh as spring flowers when you walk into a classroom on Sunday morning. (Of course, flowers don't cry for their mothers, nor sometimes throw crayons.)

At that age, you plant seeds
hard to root out in later years.
They try, some of them…in their
teens, or when they go off to college.
But many come back. Maybe not
until they have a baby of their own.
If nothing else brings them back,
that will. They don't feel
right with their kids not baptized,
or in Sunday school.

Children tie us to a church;
spring faces and spring voices that
keep belief green. Or at least,
the wish for belief…

A sober march
but youthful steps
on a sun-warmed day in May

Memories, tears
but Spring's full-leaf
and Summer is on its way

SUMMER

"And grow..."

Your kids stretch up with the crops, summers. That chubby pair that bounced off the school bus on "last day!" cast longer shadows now, and it's not all summer running. More strength in the boy's arms, and the girl's shiny head reaches closer to your shirt pocket when you close an arm around her. Yes, a time for growing. The pale shoots of spring flush with richer green, and you stride through a flowering crop and feel...if you stopped, you'd root and grow. The hot-oil smell of your engine drifts into the summer bouquet, and your wife's sun-warm fragrance reaches up to you, as she puts a cold drink in your hand. You pause, and fill your eyes with the summer richness of your land.

Real work, and Mom's food, and Mom to season it all with a laugh and make it special. Why doesn't summer last all year?

Free of walls and halls and books, free to study just for fun in real-life pages soft with grass, warmed beneath the summer sun.

It's still fun when you get a little older, but you carry more of the weight. And feel a secret pride when Dad shares confidences with you.

Summer greens on the way to supper.
A dab of spring-planted seed pays
dividends all summer long.

Thanks.
Maybe the ritual words
do just flow mechanically. But the
thought runs deep. Thanks.
Thanks for this moment…and help us
to see how really good it is.

Crops grow, kids grow, and the summer of life zips past like a line drive. In the baseball months you can use the game to get over the old lessons...play by the rules...give it your best...there's another day if you lose...

And get your glove *under* the low ones.

Mostly, it's just for fun.

We all say that, anyway. But it's more fun when you win.

Hum it in there!

First summer fruit,
and maybe the best.
Strawberries...a business for you...

...or early-summer earnings for
girls. A taste of heaven in
cream...for everybody. Strawberries.

You can't turn your back
on that lawn this time of year.
The grass shoots up.

Hay time, too. Chop it fresh,
feed it green. Or, cure, and pack
it in a silo.

Or store the sun for
winter in heavy, scratchy bales.
A smile says
the load's on the wagon.

baler can spit out a backache on a sunny afternoon. But a young man likes the test, and the hay smells sweet in the sun.

Sweating together makes work pleasure. But doggone, a hay mow can be a hot place on a summer afternoon.

The high-arching sun coaxes
row crops into their big stretch...

...while you spray and plow
and even hoe to husband moisture
and nutrients for crop plants,
not weeds. *Man*power still helps cotton,
or soybeans, or vegetables.

And real *horse*power still
earns a place in some tobacco patches,
or other small-acreage crops.

But power, big unsweating steel-lunged
power covers the big acreages.

Office in the field—the pickup truck. What farmer, manager or foreman could function without this successor to the horse and wagon?

Two-way radio made it a mobile command post. You can move a man, order a part...maybe load a plane...*now*.

Muscled-up planes and quick-handed
flyers put wings on seed, fertilizer and
chemicals...shrink job-time for planting,
spraying, fertilizing and weeding from
days to hours, hours to minutes.

No job for a pessimist…

…but you're never far from the ground.

Hot job...cool feet.
Flood it on, sprinkle it on,
or pray it out of the clouds
...*water* puts life
in your business.

Nature's applications can be a
mixed blessing. So you watch the
heavy clouds roll up with relief,
anticipation—and apprehension.
For with the big rains may come...

…hail.

"We expected a storm. Hot, muggy afternoon, with the clouds building. We had just sat down to early supper when the wind changed. The curtains stood out a little, and the breeze felt good. But I figured I'd better have a look, so I got up and walked to the door so I could see to the west. It squeezed my stomach. The black belly of the storm cloud was rolling over us, turning the day to dusk. But a glowing white veil was sweeping under it from the west… *hail!* I hollered to the boy, and we raced to get the car inside and shut the shed doors. It hit full force just as we made the back porch again. A few loud raps and pings as the first stones struck—then a machine-gun rattle on the grain bins and the steel shed—then just a solid roar. A couple windows on the west went in the first big push of wind and hail. I sent the kids to the basement and my wife and I grabbed towels and anything handy and tried to stop the water from pouring in. The house shuddered and we could hear tree limbs crack, but the worst was over in about 15 minutes. It rained on for a while, but the wind and hail let up. I pulled on a jacket and boots then, and went out to look around. I tell you it made me sick. The yard was covered with drifts of wet leaves. The trees were stripped almost bare. And the house—the hail blasted most of the paint off the west side. Same for all the wood-sided buildings. The bins and the steel shed had pits all over their windward sides and roofs, and some amazingly big dents, too.

"Then I heard my wife, mad and crying at the same time, looking at her flowers and garden. Just pounded right into the mud. I walked over and gave her a squeeze and then we walked out through the edge of the grove to look at the corn. I'd been dreading it; I knew what I'd find. And it was even worse. Hip-high corn shredded, or snapped off and beaten into the surface. Like shadows, wind shadows. Insurance? Yes, thank God, I had hail insurance. But the money wasn't all of it. I'd lost a crop. And I was glad it was still raining, so the tears didn't show on my face."

Water...it's sun-warm
and your mouth is full of grit.
But nothing ever tasted better.

Cools you inside, cools you
outside—its value climbs
with the temperature. The
town pool—that's the
"ol' swimmin' hole" these days.

Sun and water feed another summer harvest. Warm hands still sack and sort vegetables, pluck and box fruits; nestle fat melons in trucks. But increasingly, steel and rubber fingers stir through soil and vines, as growers turn to mechanical harvesters.

They're rolling...
from Texas to the Canadian border,
the combines track the summer northward
through the ripening grain.

Summer is one long wheat field...

But you wouldn't trade
that hot seat for a desk. (No blue
and gold harvest mornings in an office;
no smell of hot oil and dust,
no sweet breeze
before the sun gets high.)

Spouting augers
pass judgement on fertility,
rain and varieties.

Tests determine quality, and the
market, the government, your knowledge
and luck influence the price.
But it's "in the bin."

Some summer crops walk off the farm

...with a little help.

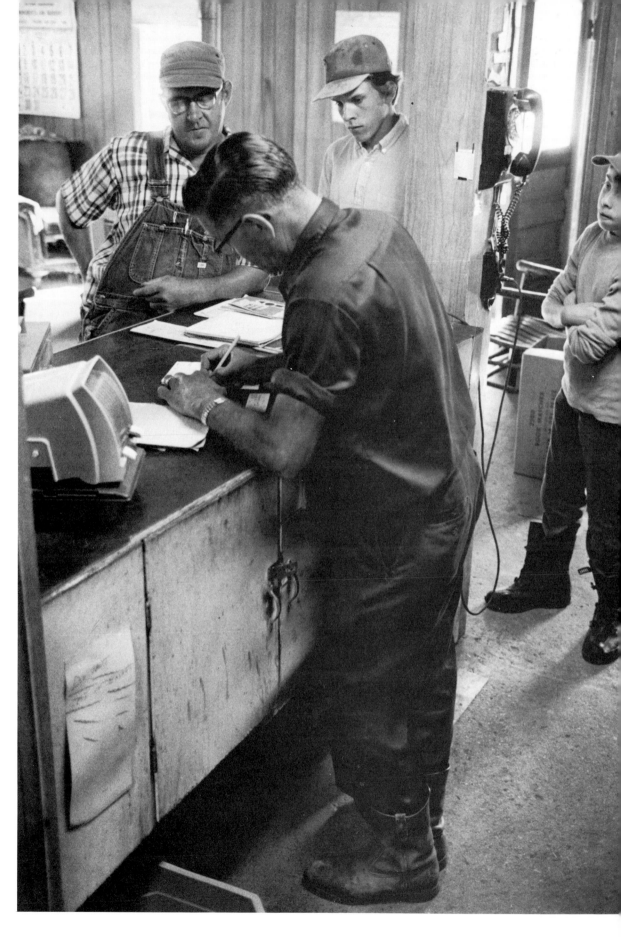

Payday. You're trading planning, labor, feed and risk for that check. You've estimated your return, but you wait expectantly for the scale and the buyer to put an actual price on your efforts.

product . . . at an auction. There's a little magic in that word. It draws us all,

moths to a candle, whether we're buying, or "just seeing how they sell."

Bid or not, you're part
of the action at an auction, riveted
by the pitch and chant of
the auctioneer...always just a finger-flick
from ownership.

You'd swear that auctioneer can spot even the *thought* of a bid.

hange the hats, change the
color of the cattle from black and white
to red and white...

...and you're filling a feedlot
instead of a milking string.

It's BIG business,
feeding cattle.

Oh, yes, much of our beef still comes from farmer feedlots. But out on the plains, the big commercial lots grow…

...and grow. Under the sun, where
the gritty soil soaks up water and
waste. But not all the smell.

So ride a little farther
upslope, up where the wind sweeps clean
under a big sky
…a horse remains
a work animal for herdsmen…

…and you can still dip
cooking water out of a spring.

Bunkhouse, cowboy, leather chaps...all still real...because they're all still needed, along with cowboy skills.

84

They start learning those skills
early around here...although you do have to
grow into the work.

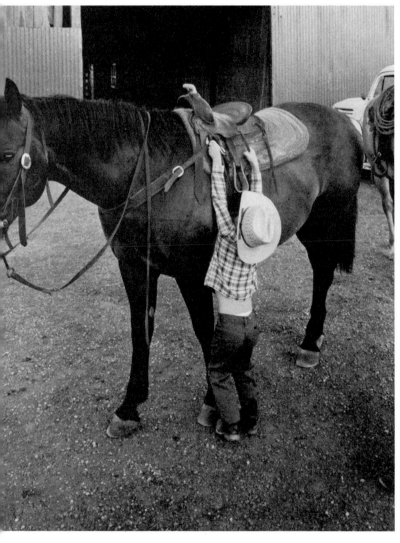 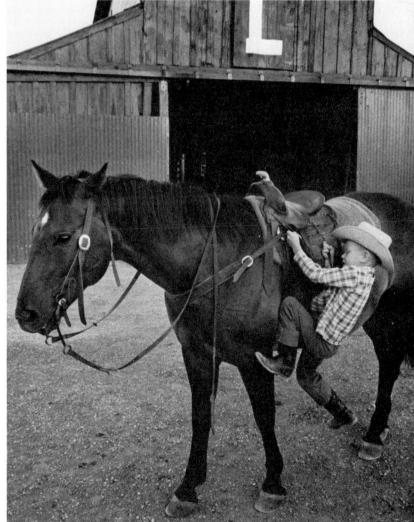

Even in the high cow country, wheels keep earning new jobs. On a new mount for a wrangler...

...or big diesel rigs that carry cattle and feed in and out.

The old chuck wagon seems to have a
new look, too.

But the faces under the big hats still show the same old toughness, humor and *independence*—essential spirit of the West.

And it comes in all sizes.

Just in case
you think these skills
get exercised only
in the rodeo arena...

...Whooee-e-e!...

...spend a few days with a crew on the range.

Easy, now, easy…

Open wide, that's it…let's get this pill down you.

Summer moves on. And you've got to have

      winter in mind, when the sun grows hot on your back, and

clip the meadows, and bale the grass

      and get it safe in the stack.

Out across the plains, the sun
glares on into deep summer,
sweeping the streets of country towns,
driving shoppers into the cool, stale breath
of air-conditioned stores.

But it takes a hot sun
to warm you through, if you've
seen enough summers.

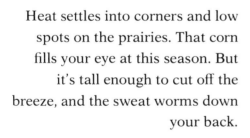

Heat settles into corners and low
spots on the prairies. That corn
fills your eye at this season. But
it's tall enough to cut off the
breeze, and the sweat worms down
your back.

Cattle crowd together in the
yellow afternoons, presenting a
collective tail to the flies

...or soaking their hocks in a pasture pond. The grass fades...

...and shoes come off. Deep summer.

First work was play.
Now play is work, sometimes.
Daydreaming days. And little thoughts
of school creeping back
into your mind.

When the "home-growns" show up,
summer is edging toward fall in the
North. (Now, "home-grown" means
from no more than one state away.)
Watermelon, the smile fruit. Well,
did you ever see a frown on a face
looking at a red, dripping slice
of watermelon? A cold slice brightens
the hot, dusty days of late summer.

L ate summer…waiting time,
time for mowing weeds, odd
jobs, extra moments to share,
or a little vacation.

Maybe best of all
when you're young—late summer
means fair time.

Walk through a day at a county fair. Budding herdsmen strain for ribbons that help grade a year's 4-H club work. They learn something about winning and losing. Simple. Winning's more fun. Losing can be practice for winning...or for more losing. You point morals that way if you're a parent, or a 4-H leader. But fairs do telescope experiences for kids, and give them a chance to practice at life a little on their own—in the show ring, around the barns; on the midway. And provide them one last fling at summer fun, before school takes up again.

You cast a practiced eye over the livestock...try out the seats on the new tractors...price a combine... sweat in the grandstand...regret the onions on your noontime foot-long hot dog...dutifully trail your wife through women's exhibits... leave your change with the midway barkers...and mentally catch your breath for a day, while you walk an ache into your back.

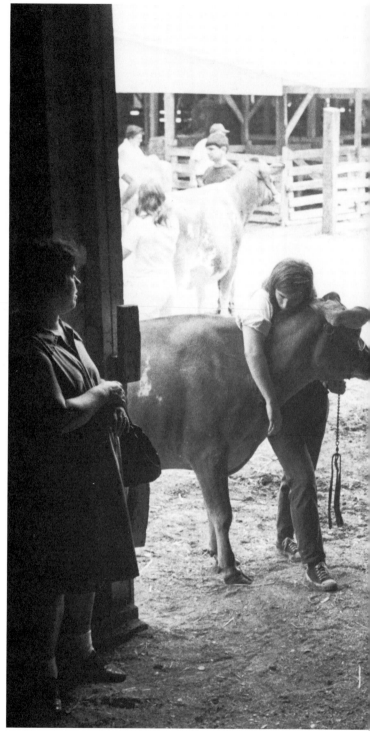

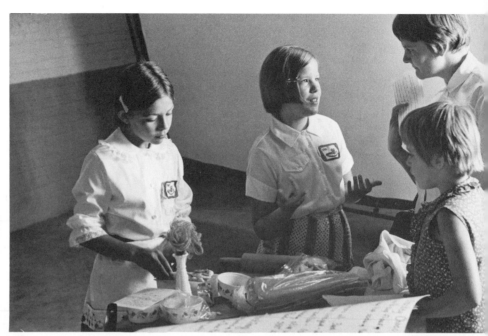

AUTUMN

"Harvest..."

Harvest enriches each day of the year someplace in America—but mostly "green harvest"—vegetables and fruits. Oh, yes, the red and green and yellow and blue and silver combines start rolling up the carpet of wheat from the South early in the summer. But harvest, brown and gold harvest, enriches autumn alone. A little smoke spices the chill dawn air, and the sweet breath of cattle lingers in frosty clouds. You tarry, longer than you should, watching them eat. A spark of excitement over the new crop, struck in late summer, glows warmer now as you nose your big harvester into the field.

A clean, sharp autumn afternoon...
you guide the snouts down rustling
rows of corn. Snap and clunk and
whir and grind strip kernels from
the heavy ears...

...and fill the waiting wagons
with a golden stream
...as molten ore
flows thickly into molds.

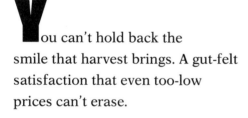

You can't hold back the smile that harvest brings. A gut-felt satisfaction that even too-low prices can't erase.

...for something
of yourself has been
returned, that season
of your life you pledged
last spring.

The calendar pushes you. But you welcome a break, and another voice. Fingers stiff from the steering wheel close readily around a sandwich.

Early and late in the field...

...or weighing
and storing the crop

orn meal, syrup,
sugar, starch...
Your corn may move a dozen ways...
into a hundred foods.
Or never leave the farm...

...except as corn-fed beef
or pork. Your eye and instinct
help you bring them on.

But livestock feeding
is more than art...

...computers, scales...

...experience...

...you also need
faith, and common sense.

Leaves rain down into
wrestling mats, and a football's a
handy excuse. Boys rub off
"confinement marks" of school like
a horse rolling away the
memory of a saddle.

After-school and
weekends offer time for clean-up jobs.
Feels good, out there in the
trees together.

…but when you've carried the
heavy end of the day, it feels good
to be back in the house, with the heat
and light and good smells of the
kitchen just through the door.

The autumn chill in the air
doesn't hurt anyone's appetite.
And for dessert—isn't that
fresh-baked apple pie you smell?

Still, little hands reveal
thoughts of a bigger feast.
And count the days
'til its coming.

You keep a
different mental count,
and crowd fall
work into shortening days.
And welcome the warm side of
flip-flop weather.

The big day arrives. Thanksgiving Day
—a "together" day, a remembering day,
a holiday.
The unofficial end of autumn.

Thick gray mornings betray the
passage of cold air over the still-
warm earth.

Barren limbs claw at a northern wind
  that soon will still the water

...or brush fall mist in a crystal
coat to beguile an early hunter.

WINTER

"And plan it all again"

Your dad said that last winter, "Boy, you won't know until you're older just how strong a man can long for spring to come 'round again. And finally, just hope to see one more spring." Well, Dad's winters were emptier, longer in earlier years. You find that planning, buying, meetings; analyzing your records, sweating over a computer printout, caring for livestock, following the kids' basketball teams— hardly leaves time to enjoy a good storm. But Dad was right. The older you get, the stronger the ache to see spring again; to start new life again. Well, no use moping. You can find a little fun in winters, too!

"Let 'er rip!"

"Expensive 'toy' for a farmer? Yes, I know they say that. Looked that way to me, before I rode with the neighbor a few times. And then got one myself. And you know what? They're right...darned expensive! But we wouldn't give up snowmobiling. It's just great. Skimming over your fields with the wind in your face kind of sets you free.

"Any more, I'm lucky to get in the saddle myself. The kids love it.

ctually, it comes in mighty handy during winter storms. Getting hay out to snowbound cattle, playing St. Bernard to people stuck out along the county road, or just getting to town before they open the highways. During our last big blizzard snowmobiles saved several lives...ferrying people to the hospital, or doctors to isolated farms.

"Well, you can come up with pretty good reasons for anything you buy, can't you? Mostly it's just for fun."

A faint breath of summer lingers in the cured alfalfa. As winter whitens the fields, you cherish the reminder of green and the memory of the sun, packed in the sweet-smelling bales. Takes weight from the hay as you load. But you welcome the cool wet feathers of snow on your work-warm face, as you break a track to the cattle.

Any wagon that hauls hay
will haul kids, too. Sometimes
on the same load. Fun lies
just the other side of work
on the farm. Or mixes with it.
The great thing about a farmer's
equipment—an idea, a laugh
or a coat of snow can transform
tractors and wagons into
"recreation vehicles."

The Christmas card scenery turns your eye
to the calendar—and spurs you into the annual December rush. Already
time for the tree. It means more if you're able to cut
your own. But any fir or pine or spruce fills your warm
rooms with a once-a-year fragrance that works a little magic.

153

Not long now.
Days shrink for parents
and other "old folks" who
must crowd in shopping, baking
and church and school events.
But time stretches
endlessly for youngsters.

However, the 25th always
follows the 24th...and most
young dreams become reality.
If you've weakened or
wondered along the way—
the results make it
seem worthwhile.

Good thing Christmas comes
early. It leaves the long
end of winter for wearing
the shine off all those presents
designed to let kids
skim over snow and ice.

The promise of hot, fresh cookies "when you get back" keeps a kid's mind off toes curling cold in his boots.

Have you ever eaten afternoon lunch on a farm? Especially a northern dairy farm? Whether it follows a romp with the kids, or is the usual stoking up before evening chores, "lunch" hardly describes the fare. It's first cousin to the smorgasbords of Scandinavia. And why not, come to think of it. Run the register of dairy-farmer names, and you sound echoes of Denmark, Norway, Sweden, Finland and Iceland. "Help yourself," your host will urge.

Cold meats—two or three kinds—with as many breads to surround them. Cheeses for sure. On a dairy farm? At least two varieties. And homemade pickles, sweet and sour. Dessert? A little something, yes. Cookies, or doughnuts, and cake and pie. Milk or fruit juice to fill empty spaces and hot black coffee to settle the meal. And good talk, and laughter. Not supper, mind you— afternoon lunch. The hot meat, potatoes and vegetables will weight the table after milking and feeding chores.

But you need fuel. You burn great gobs of energy moving feed and handling livestock and milking cows and wrestling machines. But you do notice that you're not burning up as much as you shovel in...

Even his wife's good cooking doesn't give the true stockman the satisfaction he finds in watching his animals eat. If you've shared that feeling of inner warmth, played the role of provider to your flocks and herds, you know that few pleasures surpass it. And a winter storm heightens the feeling. You smile into the wind, buck into the challenge of piling drifts, and plow through with the feed. Oh, that's not what you tell your neighbor. No, you cuss the weather and loudly envy your grain-farming friends, snug inside during winter.

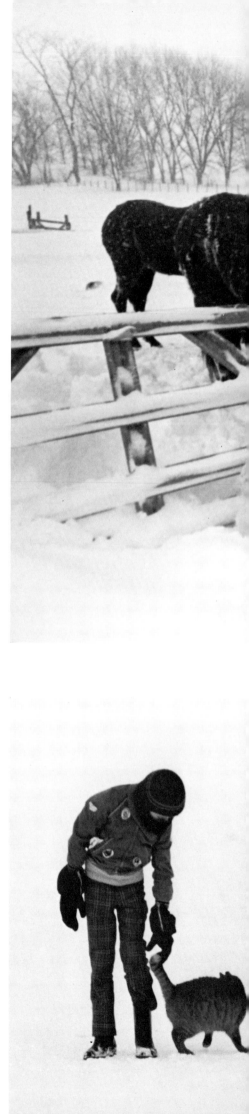

The storm-born feeling of urgency—
and the challenge and fun of the snow—
brings you chore help from the house.
Hay for the horses...and maybe
a rescuer for a cat with cold feet.

162

There! That quick glimpse of a
deer herd, frozen for a blink
against the snow, repays you somewhat for their
mooching ways. Maybe you'll buy a deer
license this season and...maybe you won't.

Working cattle, feeding
cattle, smelling cattle, selling cattle,
cussing cattle. Being a cattleman,
on the range or in a Midwest
feed lot, goes deeper than a big hat
and boots. Oh, you've earned the right
to wear these practical trappings
of an industry still dusted with romance.
The trappings stay while change rides
high. But purebreds, crossbreds,
compacts, fast-gainers...their manure
all smells the same, soaked into the
leather of your boots. They waft a
strong reminder of your profession,
as you pull them on in the morning.
It sharpens your anticipation
of the new day.

Your winter ties to livestock keep
you in short range of home. But
there's time to share with neighbors,
and common bonds draw you to stock
shows, purebred sales, an auction market.
While the auctioneer seeks bids...

"...quarter gotohalf gotohalf
gotohalf now two...

...you join the beehive of
conversation...

"Have you got your seed all bought?
...going to take delivery, or just...
no, I'm cutting back...yes, if you
trade now they say they'll...just
the poorest officiating I've ever seen
—ask Bill, he saw the game...this kid,
he...mmmm...whose calf is that..."

"...she's sold, boys!"

It does work...people governing themselves. True, some of us would rather take a step backward than take a chance. But we get the township's business done, and the county's, and the state's. And get about what we deserve, right up through Washington, D. C. A little easier to get folks together in the winter— if there isn't a basketball game, or a 4-H meeting, or icy roads.

A lot of the serious discussion
takes place before and after the
official business

...and the word gets around.
Mobility and communication helped
build astonishing American
agriculture, and continue to change
it faster than we'd choose.

Keeping up means keeping records. More—it means analyzing them, using them to direct your business and chart your future. And to convince and impress your banker. To tell the truth, it gets tiresome. But... no way to make it without the numbers.

173

"I get the computer printout every month. It gives me a running commentary on costs, and projects a breakeven price. Of course, a computer is like a baby. It will only spit up what you feed it. So...records. More records."

But when you've made the right decisions, it's a good feeling.

Two and two
don't always make four,
however. You do your best, but
maybe it just doesn't work out.
So you live with it, anyway.

Sometimes, though...sometimes it all
crosses the scale at once, and the
load gets a little heavy. You allow
yourself the bittersweet luxury of a
weak moment, and wonder "is it all
worth it?" Well, we've all bitten
that sugar-coated lemon. We know
the question...

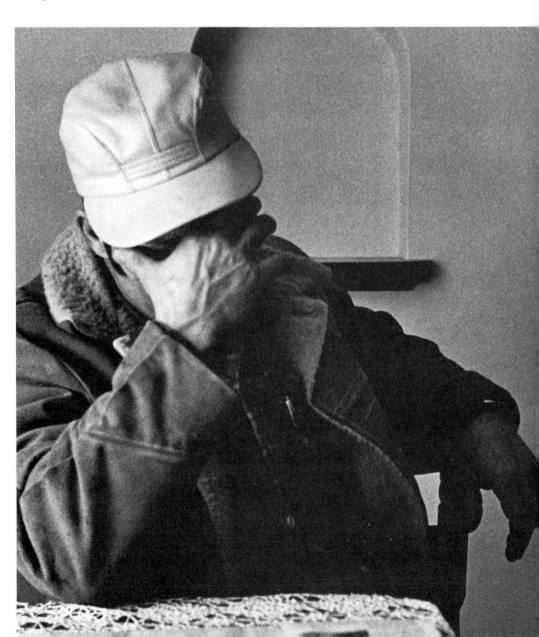

…and we know the answer.

I really didn't know
'til you,
how much I'd rather
live by two.
Or maybe even three
or four,
Heck, five or six…
OK, no more!
But I not only took
a wife,
I haltered sunshine, yes,
for life.
I really didn't know,
'til you,
how much I'd rather
live by two.

School's fun, and lunch and
gym (and boys), but the
warmth of home reaches down
the lane, and draws kids
eagerly to the kitchen—and
Mom, the one best audience
for a spiced-up replay of the day.

The farm kitchen…a lot of troubles thaw in its after-supper glow. Electric stoves and mixers (and sometimes a dishwasher) don't alter its appeal—cozy and safe as a mother's hug. A lot of tomorrows start life here, between pie and the first good television program— or homework.

Tomorrow..." if my son
stays with me, I think
we could feed 2,000 head.
He likes farming, and cattle, and
farrows sows on his own. But times
and boys' minds change. If he
stays, though..."

Wedding couples and graduates march
across its top. Sheet music papers
its side, and a young girl accompanies
her dreams on its keys. Right hand...
left hand. Will she play out her songs
under country skies? You hum and work
and wonder...

Young enough to know for sure
  you'll never leave the farm.

Young enough to know your Dad
  can always find the answer.

Young enough that a hug from Mom
  is still a darn good feeling.

Young enough that work is fun
  and helping Dad pure pleasure.

Young enough that girls are dumb
  except your baby sister.

Young enough to scoff at life
  that doesn't smell of cows.

Young enough to know you're right...
  but old enough to wonder.

I believe in Spring

I believe in Spring
not only when the sun's warm touch
pulls green from stirring seed,
and eggs erupt in velvet balls,
and new mouths suck at mother's milk
in jerky, pink-tongued greed...

I believe in Spring
not only when soft southern breath
sprays pollen through the corn,
while warblers sing and boy yells ring,
and cattle wade through soft green waves
and yellow grain is shorn...

I believe in Spring
when fire-shot winds and drumming hail
whip life from greening plants,
or sun sears leaves in yellow rage...
I know there'll be another Spring
and yet another chance.

I believe in Spring.

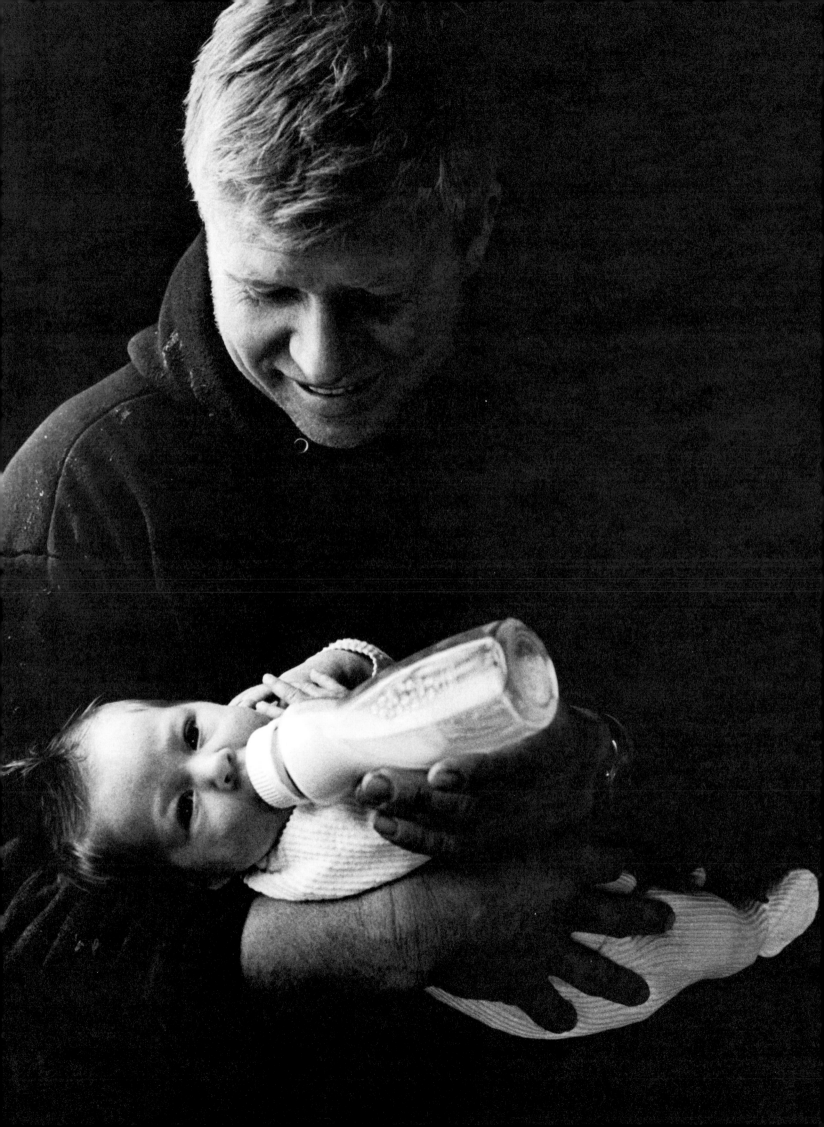